MW00904658

WWW.BENDOCKERY.COM

Copyright © 2022 B. C. Dockery

All rights reserved.

50 CHRISTMAS DUETS
VOLS. 1 - 5

CONTENTS

- JINGLE BELLS
- JOLLY OLD ST. NICHOLAS
- JOY TO THE WORLD
- LO, HOW A ROSE E'ER BLOOMING
- O COME ALL YE FAITHFUL
- O COME, O COME, EMMANUEL
- O HOLY NIGHT
- O LITTLE TOWN OF BETHLEHEM
- O TANNENBAUM (O CHRISTMAS TREE)
- ONCE IN ROYAL DAVID'S CITY
- SILENT NIGHT
- SING WE NOW OF CHRISTMAS
- STILL, STILL, STILL
- THE BIRTHDAY OF A KING
- THE FIRST NOEL
- THE FRIENDLY BEASTS
- THE HOLLY AND THE IVY
- THE SNOW LAY ON THE GROUND
- THE TWELVE DAYS OF CHRISTMAS
- TOYLAND
- UP ON THE HOUSETOP
- WASSAIL SONG
- WE THREE KINGS
- WE WISH YOU A MERRY CHRISTMAS
- WEXFORD CAROL
- WHAT CHILD IS THIS?
- WHILE SHEPHERDS WATCHED

ARRANGEMENTS BY B. C. DOCKERY ©2022

All Through the Night

Score

Traditional Welsh
B. C. Dockery

Arr. ©2022

All Through the Night

Violin 1

Traditional Welsh
B. C. Dockery

All Through the Night

Violin 2

Traditional Welsh
B. C. Dockery

All Through the Night

Piano

Traditional Welsh
B. C. Dockery

Arr. ©2022

Angels From the Realm of Glory

Score

Henry Smart
B. C. Dockery

Arr. ©2022

Angels From the Realm of Glory

Violin I

Henry Smart
B. C. Dockery

Angels From the Realm of Glory

Violin II

Henry Smart
B. C. Dockery

Arr. ©2022

Angels From the Realm of Glory

Piano

Henry Smart
B. C. Dockery

Arr. ©2022

Away in a Manger

James R. Murray
arr. B C Dockery

Violin I

Away in a Manger

James R. Murray
arr. B C Dockery

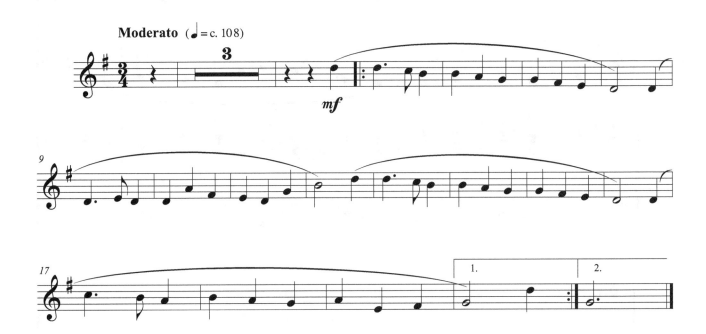

Violin II

Away in a Manger

James R. Murray
arr. B C Dockery

Piano

Away in a Manger

James R. Murray
arr. B C Dockery

Away in a Manger (Cradle Song)

William J. Kirkpatrick
arr. B C Dockery

Away in a Manger (Cradle Song)

Away in a Manger (Cradle Song)

Violin I

William J. Kirkpatrick
arr. B C Dockery

Away in a Manger (Cradle Song)

Violin II

William J. Kirkpatrick
arr. B C Dockery

Away in a Manger (Cradle Song)

Piano

William J. Kirkpatrick
arr. B C Dockery

Bring a Torch, Jeanette Isabella

Score

Traditional French

B. C. Dockery

Arr. ©2022

Bring a Torch, Jeanette Isabella

Violin 1

Traditional French
B. C. Dockery

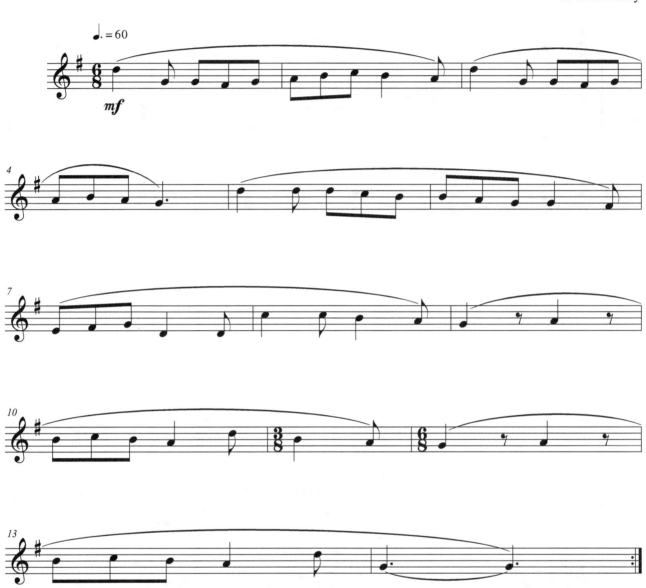

Bring a Torch, Jeanette Isabella

Violin 2

Traditional French
B. C. Dockery

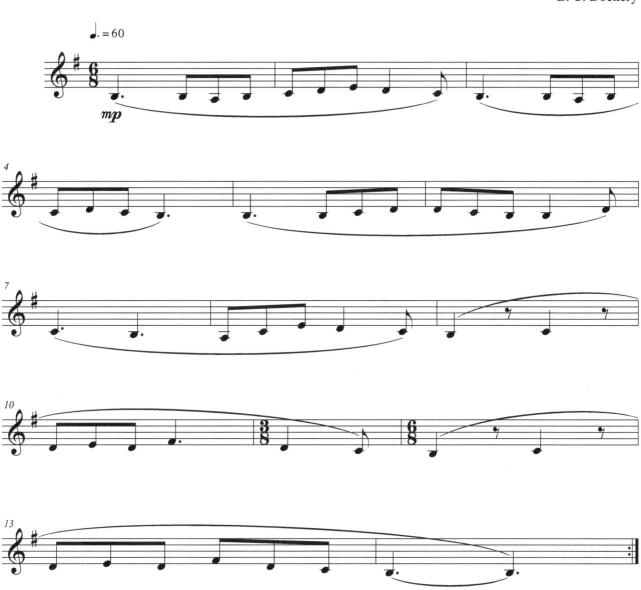

Bring a Torch, Jeanette Isabella

Piano

Traditional French
B. C. Dockery

Carol of the Bells

Mykola Leonovych
arr. B. C. Dockery

Violin I
Carol of the Bells

Mykola Leonovych
arr. B. C. Dockery

Carol of the Bells

Violin II

Mykola Leonovych
arr. B. C. Dockery

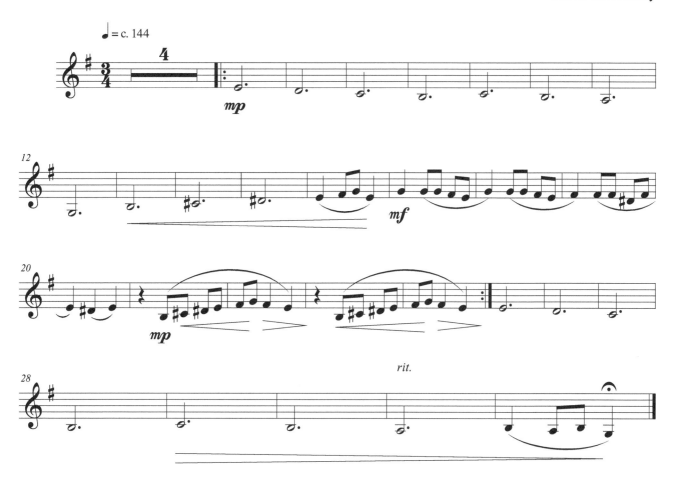

Carol of the Bells

Piano

Mykola Leonovych
arr. B. C. Dockery

Christ was Born on Christmas Day

Score

Traditional
B. C. Dockery

Arr. ©2022

Christ was Born on Christmas Day

Violin 1

Traditional
B. C. Dockery

Christ was Born on Christmas Day

Violin 2

Traditional
B. C. Dockery

Christ was Born on Christmas Day

Piano

Traditional

B. C. Dockery

Christians, Awake

Score

John Wainwright
B. C. Dockery

Arr. ©2022

Christians, Awake

Christians, Awake

Violin 1

John Wainwright
B. C. Dockery

Christians, Awake

Violin 2

John Wainwright
B. C. Dockery

Christians, Awake

Piano

John Wainwright
B. C. Dockery

Coventry Carol

Score

Traditional
B. C. Dockery

Arr. ©2022

Coventry Carol

Violin 1

Traditional
B. C. Dockery

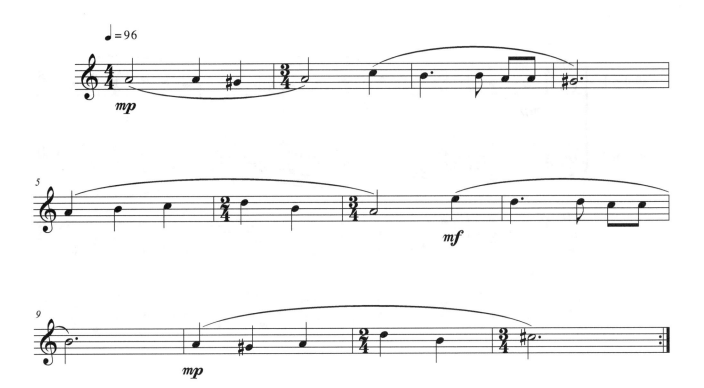

Coventry Carol

Violin 2

Traditional
B. C. Dockery

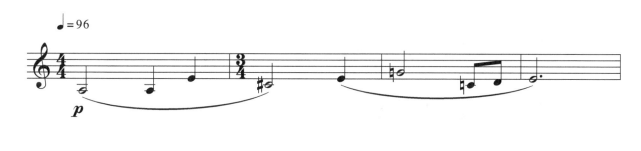

Coventry Carol

Piano

Traditional
B. C. Dockery

Dance of the Sugar Plum Fairy

Tchaikovsky
arr. B. C. Dockery

Violin I

Dance of the Sugar Plum Fairy

Tchaikovsky
arr. B. C. Dockery

Violin II

Dance of the Sugar Plum Fairy

Tchaikovsky
arr. B. C. Dockery

Piano

Dance of the Sugar Plum Fairy

Tchaikovsky
arr. B. C. Dockery

Deck the Halls

Old Welsh Air
arr. B. C. Dockery

Violin I

Deck the Halls

Old Welsh Air
arr. B. C. Dockery

Violin II

Deck the Halls

Old Welsh Air
arr. B. C. Dockery

Piano

Deck the Halls

Old Welsh Air
arr. B. C. Dockery

Ding Dong Merilly on High

Score

Traditional
B. C. Dockery

Arr. ©2022

Ding Dong Merilly on High

Ding Dong Merilly on High

Violin 1

Traditional
B. C. Dockery

Arr. ©2022

Ding Dong Merilly on High

Violin 2

Traditional
B. C. Dockery

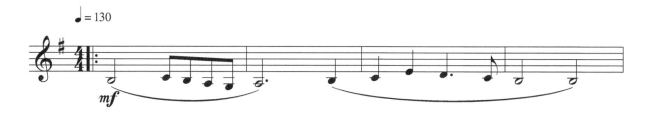

Ding Dong Merilly on High

Piano

Traditional

B. C. Dockery

Gaudete

Score

Traditional
B. C. Dockery

Gaudete

Vln. 1

Vln. 2

D.C. al Fine

Vln. 1

Vln. 2

D.C. al Fine

D.C. al Fine

D.C. al Fine

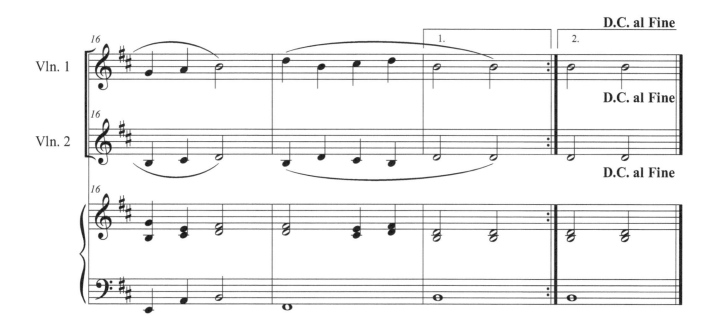

Gaudete

Violin 1

Traditional
B. C. Dockery

Gaudete

Violin 2

Traditional
B. C. Dockery

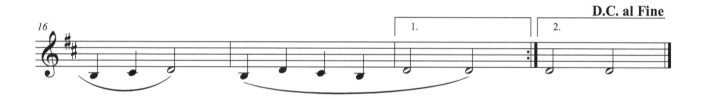

Gaudete

Piano

Traditional
B. C. Dockery

Gesu Bambino

Score

Pietro Yon

B. C. Dockery

Arr. ©2022

Gesu Bambino

Gesu Bambino

Violin I

Pietro Yon
B. C. Dockery

Gesu Bambino

Violin II

Pietro Yon
B. C. Dockery

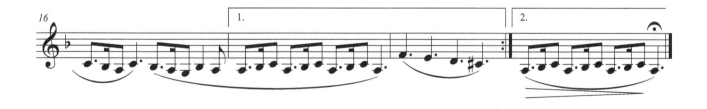

Arr. ©2022

Gesu Bambino

Piano

Pietro Yon
B. C. Dockery

God Rest Ye Merry Gentlemen

Traditional
arr. B. C. Dockery

Violin I

God Rest Ye Merry Gentlemen

Traditional
arr. B. C. Dockery

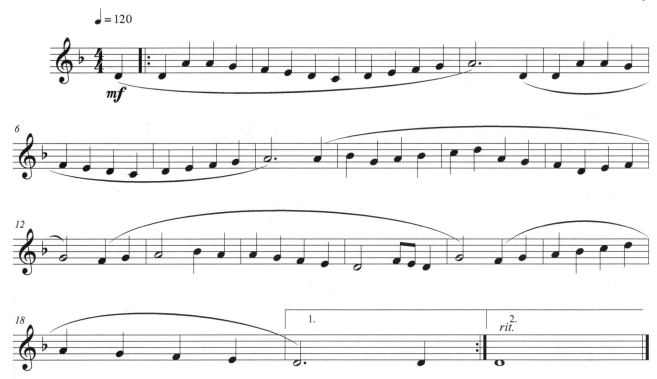

Violin II
God Rest Ye Merry Gentlemen

Traditional
arr. B. C. Dockery

God Rest Ye Merry Gentlemen

Piano

Traditional
arr. B. C. Dockery

Good Christian Men, Rejoice!

Score

Traditional German
B. C. Dockery

Arr. ©2022

Good Christian Men, Rejoice!

Violin I

Traditional German
B. C. Dockery

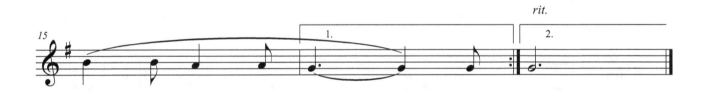

Arr. ©2022

Good Christian Men, Rejoice!

Violin II

Traditional German
B. C. Dockery

Good Christian Men, Rejoice!

Piano

Traditional German
B. C. Dockery

Good King Wenceslas

Traditional
arr. B. C. Dockery

Allegro (M.M. ♩ = c. 120)

Violin I

Good King Wenceslas

Traditional
arr. B. C. Dockery

Violin II

Good King Wenceslas

Traditional
arr. B. C. Dockery

Piano

Good King Wenceslas

Traditional
arr. B. C. Dockery

Hark, the Herald Angels Sing

Felix Mendelssohn
arr. B. C. Dockery

Hark, the Herald Angels Sing

Hark, the Herald Angels Sing

Violin I

Felix Mendelssohn
arr. B. C. Dockery

Violin II

Hark, the Herald Angels Sing

Felix Mendelssohn
arr. B. C. Dockery

Piano

Hark, the Herald Angels Sing

Felix Mendelssohn
arr. B. C. Dockery

I Heard the Bells on Christmas Day

Jean Baptiste Calkin
arr. B. C. Dockery

I Heard the Bells on Christmas Day

Violin I

Jean Baptiste Calkin
arr. B. C. Dockery

I Heard the Bells on Christmas Day

Violin II

Jean Baptiste Calkin
arr. B. C. Dockery

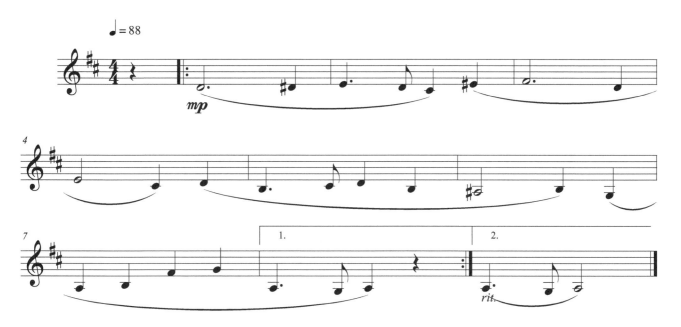

I Heard the Bells on Christmas Day

Piano

Jean Baptiste Calkin
arr. B. C. Dockery

I Saw Three Ships

Traditional English
arr. B. C. Dockery

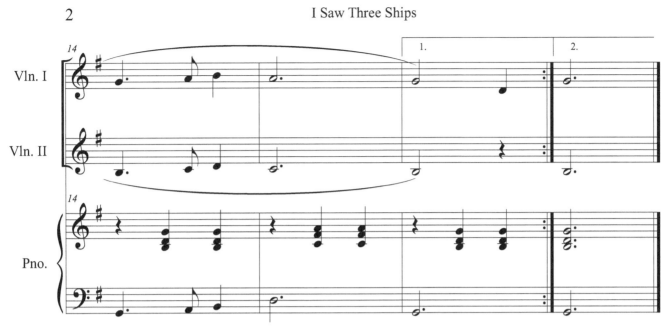

I Saw Three Ships

Violin I

Traditional English
arr. B. C. Dockery

I Saw Three Ships

Violin II

Traditional English
arr. B. C. Dockery

I Saw Three Ships

Piano

Traditional English
arr. B. C. Dockery

In the Bleak Midwinter

Gustav Holst
arr. B. C. Dockery

Violin I

In the Bleak Midwinter

Gustav Holst
arr. B. C. Dockery

Violin II

In the Bleak Midwinter

Gustav Holst
arr. B. C. Dockery

In the Bleak Midwinter

Piano

Gustav Holst
arr. B. C. Dockery

Infant Holy, Infant Lowly

Polish Carol
arr. B. C. Dockery

Infant Holy, Infant Lowly

Violin I

Polish Carol
arr. B. C. Dockery

Violin II

Infant Holy, Infant Lowly

Polish Carol
arr. B. C. Dockery

Infant Holy, Infant Lowly

Piano

Polish Carol
arr. B. C. Dockery

It Came Upon the Midnight Clear

Richard Storrs Willis
arr. B. C. Dockery

It Came Upon the Midnight Clear

It Came Upon the Midnight Clear

Violin I

Richard Storrs Willis
arr. B. C. Dockery

Violin II

It Came Upon the Midnight Clear

Richard Storrs Willis
arr. B. C. Dockery

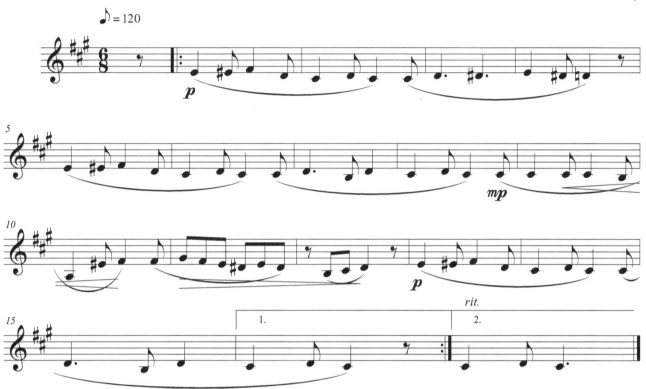

©2021

It Came Upon the Midnight Clear

Piano

Richard Storrs Willis
arr. B. C. Dockery

Jingle Bells

James Pierpont

Jingle Bells

Jingle Bells

Violin I

James Pierpont

Violin II

Jingle Bells

James Pierpont

♩ = c. 180

mp

©2020

Piano

Jingle Bells

James Pierpont

Jingle Bells

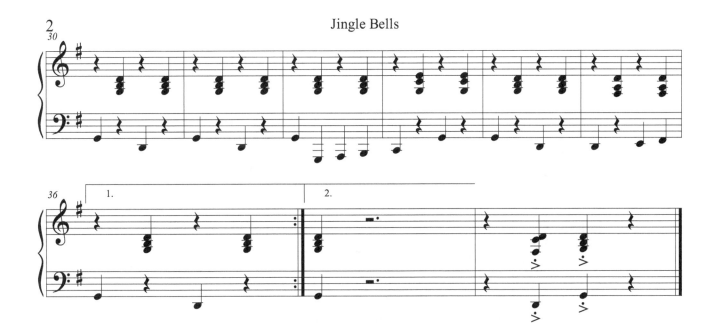

Jolly Old St. Nicholas

James R. Murray
arr. B. C. Dockery

Violin I

Jolly Old St. Nicholas

James R. Murray
arr. B. C. Dockery

Violin II

Jolly Old St. Nicholas

James R. Murray
arr. B. C. Dockery

Jolly Old St. Nicholas

James R. Murray
arr. B. C. Dockery

Piano

Joy to the World

Handel
arr. B C Dockery

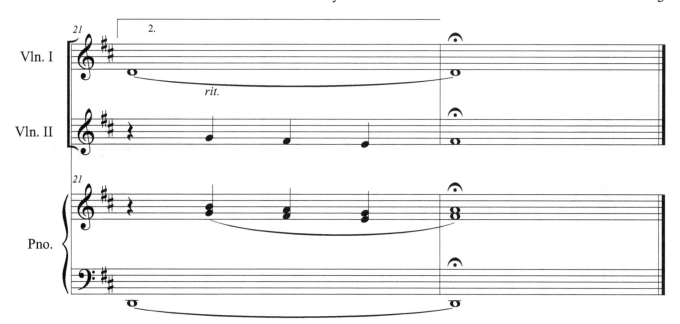

Violin I

Joy to the World

Handel
arr. B C Dockery

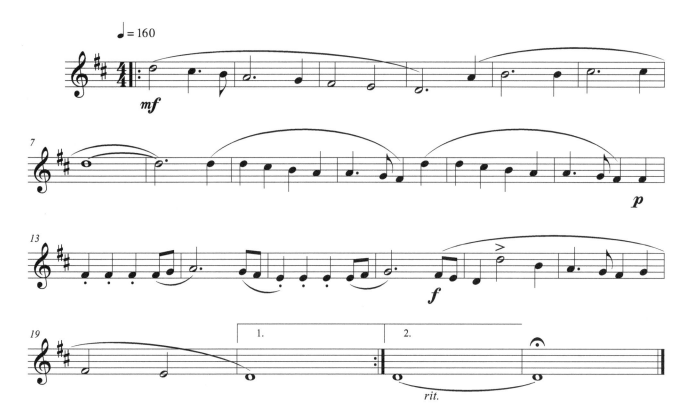

Violin II

Joy to the World

Handel
arr. B C Dockery

Joy to the World

Piano

Handel
arr. B C Dockery

Lo, How a Rose E'er Blooming

Score

Traditional
B. C. Dockery

Arr. ©2022

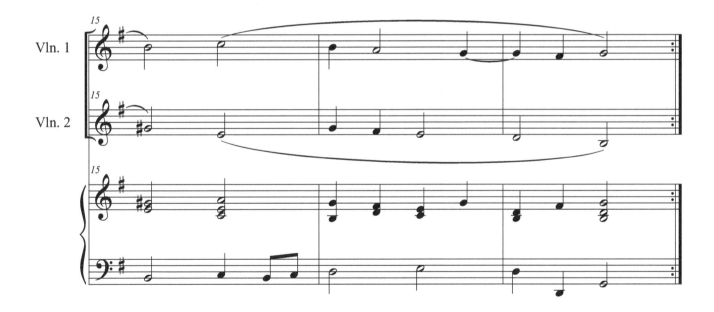

Lo, How a Rose E'er Blooming

Violin 1

Traditional
B. C. Dockery

Arr. ©2022

Lo, How a Rose E'er Blooming

Violin 2

Traditional
B. C. Dockery

Arr. ©2022

Lo, How a Rose E'er Blooming

Piano

Traditional
B. C. Dockery

O Come All Ye Faithful

John Francis Wade
arr. B C Dockery

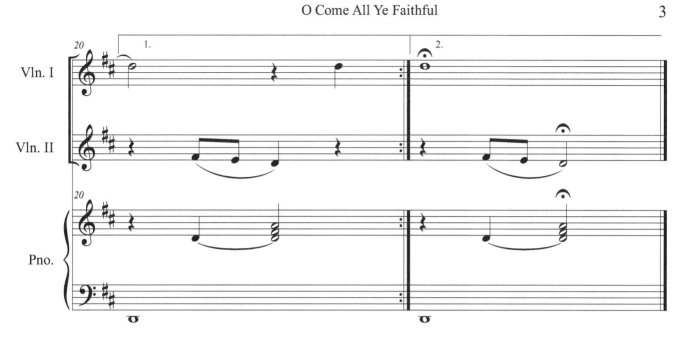

O Come All Ye Faithful

Violin I

John Francis Wade
arr. B C Dockery

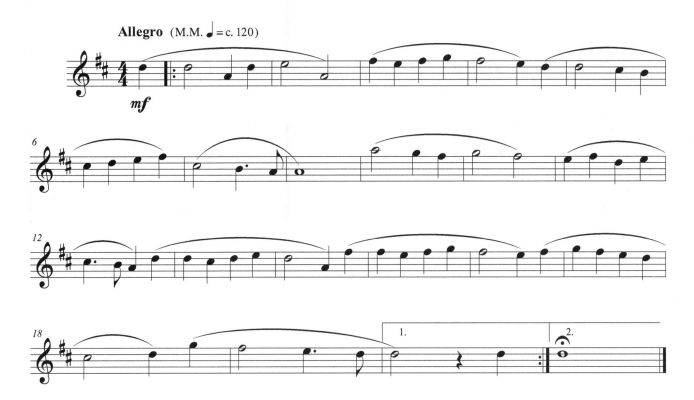

Violin II

O Come All Ye Faithful

John Francis Wade
arr. B C Dockery

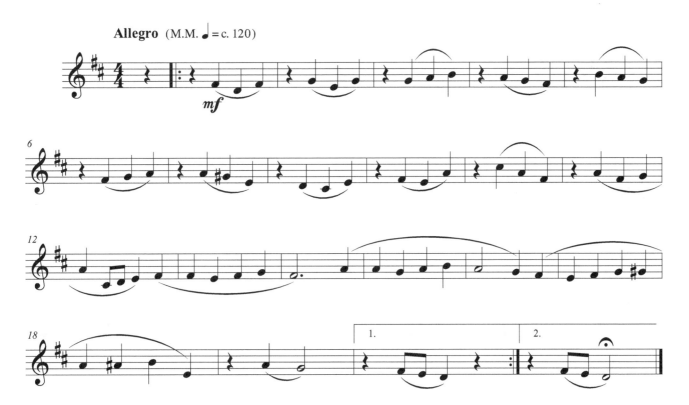

O Come All Ye Faithful

Piano

John Francis Wade
arr. B C Dockery

O Come, O Come, Emmanuel

Plainsong
arr. B. C. Dockery

O Come, O Come, Emmanuel

Violin I

Plainsong
arr. B. C. Dockery

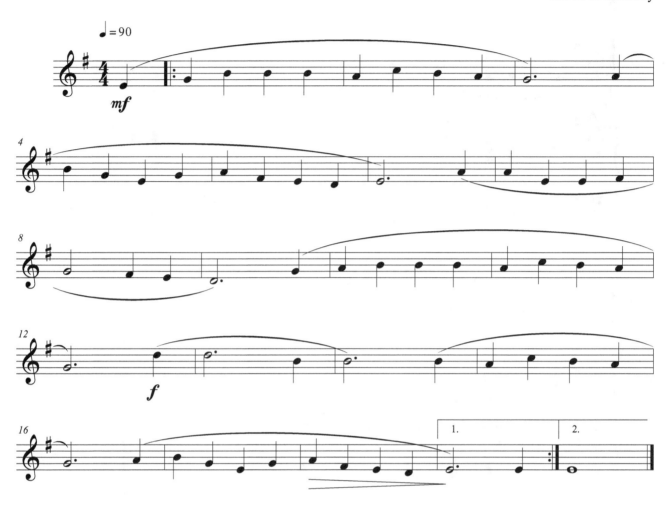

O Come, O Come, Emmanuel

Violin II

Plainsong
arr. B. C. Dockery

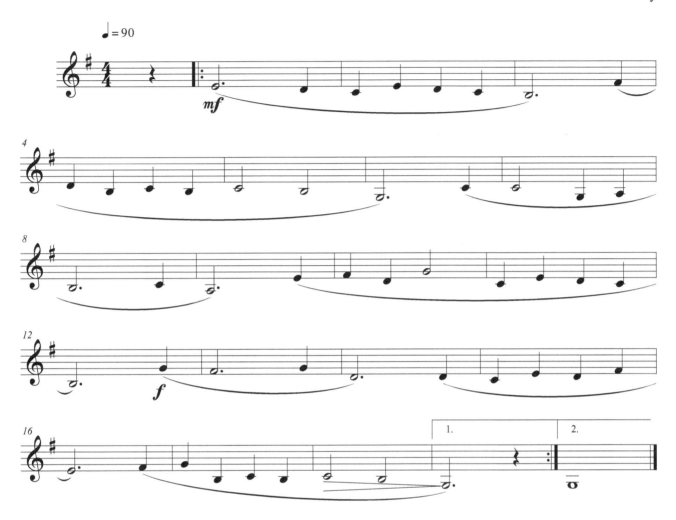

O Come, O Come, Emmanuel

Piano

Plainsong
arr. B. C. Dockery

O Holy Night

Adolphe Adam
B C Dockery

O Holy Night

Violin I

O Holy Night

Adolphe Adam
B C Dockery

O Holy Night

Violin II

Adolphe Adam
B C Dockery

O Holy Night

Piano

Adolphe Adam
B C Dockery

O Holy Night

O Little Town of Bethlehem

Lewis H. Redner
arr. B. C. Dockery

O Little Town of Bethlehem

Violin I

Lewis H. Redner
arr. B. C. Dockery

O Little Town of Bethlehem

Violin II

Lewis H. Redner
arr. B. C. Dockery

O Little Town of Bethlehem

Piano

Lewis H. Redner
arr. B. C. Dockery

O Christmas Tree

Score

O Tannenbaum

Traditional German
B. C. Dockery

Arr. ©2022

O Christmas Tree

O Christmas Tree

O Tannenbaum

Violin I

Traditional German
B. C. Dockery

O Christmas Tree

O Tannenbaum

Violin II

Traditional German
B. C. Dockery

O Christmas Tree

O Tannenbaum

Traditional German

B. C. Dockery

Piano

Once In Royal David's City

Henry J. Gauntlett
arr. B. C. Dockery

Violin I

Once In Royal David's City

Henry J. Gauntlett
arr. B. C. Dockery

Violin II

Once In Royal David's City

Henry J. Gauntlett
arr. B. C. Dockery

Piano

Once In Royal David's City

Henry J. Gauntlett
arr. B. C. Dockery

Silent Night

Franz Gruber
arr. B C Dockery

Silent Night

Franz Gruber
arr. B C Dockery

Violin I

Violin II

Silent Night

Franz Gruber
arr. B C Dockery

Silent Night

Piano

Franz Gruber
arr. B C Dockery

Sing We Now of Christmas

French Carol
arr. B. C. Dockery

Sing We Now of Christmas

Violin I

French Carol
arr. B. C. Dockery

Sing We Now of Christmas

Violin II

French Carol
arr. B. C. Dockery

Sing We Now of Christmas

Piano

French Carol
arr. B. C. Dockery

Still, Still, Still

Traditiona Austrian Carol
arr. B. C. Dockery

Still, Still, Still

Violin I

Still, Still, Still

Traditiona Austrian Carol
arr. B. C. Dockery

Violin II

Still, Still, Still

Traditiona Austrian Carol
arr. B. C. Dockery

Still, Still, Still

Piano

Traditiona Austrian Carol
arr. B. C. Dockery

The Birthday of a King

Score

William Harold Neidlinger

B. C. Dockery

Arr. ©2022

The Birthday of a King

The Birthday of a King

Violin 1

William Harold Neidlinger

B. C. Dockery

The Birthday of a King

Violin 2

William Harold Neidlinger
B. C. Dockery

The Birthday of a King

Piano

William Harold Neidlinger
B. C. Dockery

The First Noel

Traditional
arr. B C Dockery

The First Noel

The First Noel

Violin I

Traditional
arr. B C Dockery

Violin II

The First Noel

Traditional
arr. B C Dockery

Piano

The First Noel

Traditional
arr. B C Dockery

The Friendly Beasts

Score

Pierre de Corbeil
B. C. Dockery

Arr. ©2022

The Friendly Beasts

Violin 1

Pierre de Corbeil

B. C. Dockery

Arr. ©2022

The Friendly Beasts

Violin 2

Pierre de Corbeil
B. C. Dockery

The Friendly Beasts

Piano

Pierre de Corbeil
B. C. Dockery

The Holly and the Ivy

Traditional English
B. C. Dockery

Score

The Holly and the Ivy

The Holly and the Ivy

Violin 1

Traditional English
B. C. Dockery

The Holly and the Ivy

Violin 2

Traditional English
B. C. Dockery

The Holly and the Ivy

Piano

Traditional English
B. C. Dockery

The Snow Lay on the Ground

Score

Traditional

B. C. Dockery

Arr. ©2022

The Snow Lay on the Ground

The Snow Lay on the Ground

Violin 1

Traditional
B. C. Dockery

Arr. ©2022

The Snow Lay on the Ground

Violin 2

Traditional
B. C. Dockery

The Snow Lay on the Ground

Piano

Traditional
B. C. Dockery

The Twelve Days of Christmas

The Twelve Days of Christmas

The Twelve Days of Christmas

6-12

repeat as needed

The Twelve Days of Christmas

Violin I

Traditional English Carol
arr. B. C. Dockery

The Twelve Days of Christmas

Violin II

Traditional English Carol
arr. B. C. Dockery

The Twelve Days of Christmas

Piano

Traditional English Carol
arr. B. C. Dockery

The Twelve Days of Christmas

Toyland

Score

Victor Herbert
B. C. Dockery

Arr. ©2022

Toyland

Violin 1

Victor Herbert
B. C. Dockery

Arr. ©2022

Toyland

Violin 2

Victor Herbert
B. C. Dockery

Toyland

Piano

Victor Herbert

B. C. Dockery

Up on the Housetop

Score

Benjamin Hanby

B. C. Dockery

Arr. ©2022

Up on the Housetop

Violin 1

Benjamin Hanby
B. C. Dockery

Up on the Housetop

Violin 2

Benjamin Hanby
B. C. Dockery

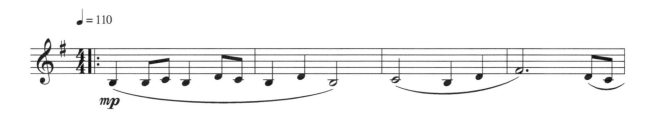

Up on the Housetop

Piano

Benjamin Hanby
B. C. Dockery

Here We Come A-Caroling

Score

Wassail Song

Traditional English

B. C. Dockery

Arr. ©2022

Here We Come A-Caroling

Violin I

Wassail Song

Traditional English
B. C. Dockery

Arr. ©2022

2

Here We Come A-Caroling

Wassail Song

Violin II

Traditional English
B. C. Dockery

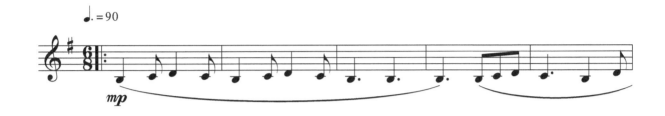

Arr. ©2022

2

Here We Come A-Caroling

Wassail Song

Piano

Traditional English

B. C. Dockery

We Three Kings

John Henry Hopkins, Jr.
arr. B C Dockery

We Three Kings

Violin I

We Three Kings

John Henry Hopkins, Jr.
arr. B C Dockery

Violin II

We Three Kings

John Henry Hopkins, Jr.
arr. B C Dockery

We Three Kings

Piano

John Henry Hopkins, Jr.
arr. B C Dockery

We Wish You A Merry Christmas

Traditional English Carol
arr. B. C. Dockery

We Wish You A Merry Christmas

Violin I

We Wish You A Merry Christmas

Traditional English Carol
arr. B. C. Dockery

Violin II

We Wish You A Merry Christmas

Traditional English Carol
arr. B. C. Dockery

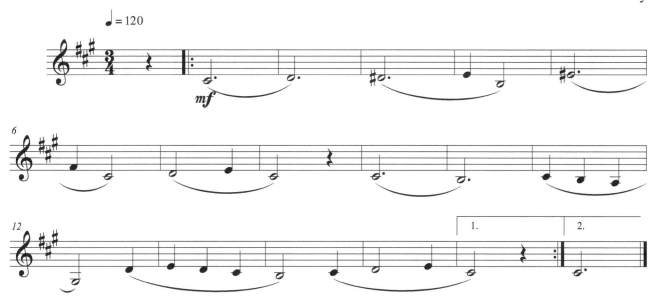

Piano

We Wish You A Merry Christmas

Traditional English Carol
arr. B. C. Dockery

The Wexford Carol

Traditional
arr. B. C. Dockery

The Wexford Carol

Violin I

The Wexford Carol

Traditional
arr. B. C. Dockery

Violin II

The Wexford Carol

Traditional
arr. B. C. Dockery

The Wexford Carol

Piano

Traditional
arr. B. C. Dockery

What Child Is This (Greensleeves)

Traditional
arr. B C Dockery

What Child Is This (Greensleeves)

What Child Is This (Greensleeves)

Violin I

Traditional
arr. B C Dockery

What Child Is This (Greensleeves)

Violin II

Traditional
arr. B C Dockery

Piano

What Child Is This (Greensleeves)

Traditional
arr. B C Dockery

While Shepherds Watched Their Flock

Score

Nahum Tate
B. C. Dockery

Arr. ©2022

While Shepherds Watched Their Flock

Violin 1

Nahum Tate

B. C. Dockery

While Shepherds Watched Their Flock

Violin 2

Nahum Tate
B. C. Dockery

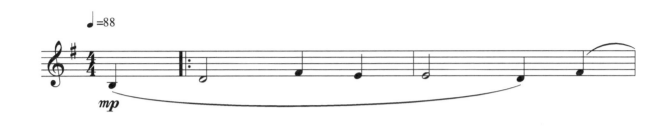

Arr. ©2022

While Shepherds Watched Their Flock

Piano

Nahum Tate
B. C. Dockery

Made in United States
Troutdale, OR
12/02/2024